ON THE DAY
THE WORLD BEGAN

by Geraldine McCaughrean

Illustrated by Norman Bancroft-Hunt

LONGMAN

CHAPTER 1

Adrift

One day in time, and at one turn of the tide, there arose such weather as whirled the world around and washed out of shape both time and tide. The Past presented itself where it was least expected. The calendar months were derailed, all twelve, shunting May into March and August into autumn. The globe, like a rubbed balloon, clung to the sky by electrical magic. Tides tugged icebergs and islands about the great circles of the Earth. And men and women from all times and places dreamed they were blown like the leaves from the trees and squandered across the ocean.

In a sleep-rumpled sea beneath a blanketing fog, a small raft tossed and turned – a square of planks such as Noah might have used for a gangplank. A hand reached over its edge and fumbled for a hold. Then another on the other side. Out from between twenty different waves, a whole shoal of swimmers closed on the raft and began to pull themselves aboard, gasping and choking. Each was startled to see the others, but it was no time to pick or choose one's companions.

"What kind of storm was that?" said a girl with hair as crinkled as the waves. "I was diving for sponges in a clear blue sea and suddenly … the water so cold … and where is my island?"

"Your island! Where's my ship? There I was, steering South, with the midnight sun behind me. Now my warriors are all lost and their arms and armour with them! *Where is my longship?*"

"Your longship! Where's my bathyscope? Let me get hold of that weather forecaster! Not a word of warning about a storm! Not one word!"

"I will bend to my fate," said a young woman with eyes the shape of almonds. "But it is hard to go to sleep in safety and wake in such peril. Yesterday my father's junk was anchored off Yokohama. Was it a typhoon that blew it out here and sank us?"

"What is this place?" said a red-skinned woman wrapped in a sodden blanket. "I have seen wide rivers before, but never one so wide and never one of this colour and never one with such a taste." She spat out some salty water.

"Well, I think it's a miracle we all found this raft," said a jolly man in clerical clothes, the pencils in his breast pocket ranged like organ pipes. "Jolly lucky, I'd say, wouldn't you?"

"The world has melted away and you talk of luck?" demanded a beautiful woman whose skin was darker than the rainclouds overhead. "One moment I'm looking out for my chook's eggs, watching a cloud pass over, small like my hand. Next minute, the world cracks open like an egg and down I fall into this ... swill. And you talk of luck?"

"Better not to ask what is past – the philosophers say – but what is to come," said the Chinaman softly, though few people heard him. Only the woolly-haired, square-faced aboriginal sitting alongside him responded. "It's plain to me we are come again into the Dream Time, like the morning of the world."

"The Dream Time, yes," said the red-skinned woman, understanding him though they came from opposite sides of the world.

"There is a perfectly rational explanation for all this," said the scientist. "A fluke of the weather. Highly interesting, I agree. Intellectually puzzling, but easily explained once we find out the facts. I shall research it. I shall make notes. This could really put me on the map in scientific circles – articles, books, lecture tours ... "

He snatched a pencil out of the cleric's pocket and began to write on the soft, wet planks of the raft.

He wrote (for lack of any other facts) a list of his fellow passengers. They numbered a tobacconist from China, a cotton-picker from Ancient Egypt, a Maori from New Zealand, a religious gentleman from Britain and a peasant from Central America. There was a Japanese girl and a Melanesian sponge-diver, a Navaho blanket-weaver from the North American Indians and a silversmith from India. There were two Africans, a Siberian, an Arabian Muslim and a Viking warrior.

"Let us pray," declared the cleric. "No! Let's take stock first. What emergency rations do we have with us? First aid? Flares? A drop of brandy? A sail? Grub?" They pooled what they had. It did not amount to very much: seven pencils, a blanket, one spear, two magical amulets, one war-axe, a Bible and an egg.

"One egg. Is that it?" asked the scientist disgustedly.

Panic stirred them at the sight of that one egg. Fifteen people adrift in the ocean and no more food between them than an egg?

"How long does it take for a person to starve?" they wondered, jumping to their feet to scan the horizon for a ship or a piece of land. The movement set the raft pitching, so that water sluiced over it and the solitary egg began to roll towards the edge.

The Japanese girl, catching it in one gentle hand, held it up between finger and thumb. "Is it so little? One egg?" she asked, in a soothing, intriguing voice. "Didn't the whole world come from just one egg?" They all looked round at her.

She was going to tell them a story. There is something about the promise of a story which soothes and calms and cheers. Suddenly the listener is a child again, cradled in its mother's arms or balanced on its father's knee. A story is coming, and with it a

curtain of words to shut out the night and the fright. When your eyes are closed, the story is all that matters. One by one, the voyagers aboard the raft sat down again and shut their eyes, the better to listen.

CHAPTER 2

Beneath the Rainbow Bridge

"It was an egg without a shell, but an egg all the same. All the makings of the world swirled inside that egg. Darkness, like a chicken, sat brood over it. White and yolk separated. Indeed, the whole egg split in hatching. Clear albumen rose up to form Heaven: the heavy yolk sank down. At the very base of the universe the Land of Yomi was formed – cold, rock-hard and deep as bass note G.

"So different and so far apart were top and bottom that they might have stayed apart for ever. Suddenly there appeared, like the single stroke of the artist's brush, a hollow reed joining the two. The reed turned to hollow bone, put on flesh and muscle, hair and clothes, and there stood Kuni-toko-tachi, the Creator.

"He set about making Heaven in the upper portion of the universe, and gods to live there, high in the pure palaces of air. Clouds and distance hid everything below them. They never even gave it a thought. Until one day Izanagi and Izanami, walking hand in hand across the Rainbow Bridge, paused to kiss and to talk.

"'What do you suppose is down there?' asked Izanami, peering over the edge.

"'Water. Darkness. Chaos. Nothing good, I suppose.' Izanagi reached down anyway with his spear and shredded a hole in the clouds so that they could see better. The spear's tip was studded with jewels which caught and refracted the colours of the rainbow. The clouds parted and there below was the faint green swell of water and the smell of salt. Izanagi reached down further and further, until at last his spear-point actually touched the water. As he lifted out the blade, the drops that fell from its tip were syrupy and thick. They clung together, until a piece of spongy land the shape of a spearhead stood at the sea's centre, with waves breaking all around. 'Oh! A little spot all of our own!' cried Izanami. 'Do let's go down there!'

"So they climbed down the spear on to the island which immediately grew green grass, plush and welcoming. The sea around, lit by their cloaks of light, glittered and turned azure blue. The two were thrilled with their secret hideaway … but a little embarrassed to find themselves – oh how shocking! – unmarried and unchaperoned. So Izanagi built a pillar in the centre of the island – a token 'meeting place'. Izanami immediately darted behind it and, emerging the other side, threw up her hands in mock astonishment. 'Oh! A handsome boy! Fancy that!'

"Izanagi blushed scarlet. '*You* can't say that! The man has to say that! Kindly keep your place in future, my dear.' So, while Izanami stood with her eyes turned shyly down, Izanagi went behind the pillar and came out again. 'Oh goodness! A pretty maiden! What a happy accident to meet her here so unexpectedly. Gracious!'

"After this they considered themselves properly introduced. Izanagi asked if he might marry Izanami. Izanami said he could. They built a house then – its roof held up by that first, useful pillar – and set about improving the small world they had begun.

"Izanami gave birth to some truly amazing children: trees and crops and flowers, animals wearing fur and hide and scales, and small, miscellaneous creatures for them to eat. Others of her children swam in the nearby ocean – giant whales and pretty little fish who plopped and shoaled in the silence of the night. She gave birth to vines, and made a crown for her husband of grapes and vine leaves. She bore whole rivers and inland seas, round islands and tribes of little people to farm them. But the feeble little humans, with no fur or hide to keep them warm, shivered in the twilight of those Early Days.

"So last of all, Izanami gave birth to Fire, for the sake of the little people: such a dangerous, generous, painful birth that it took her last drop of strength. And not all the tears that Izanagi could shed kept his wife's soul from slipping away – down, down as deep as the Land of Yomi, country of the dead.

"'No! Don't leave me! I can't bear it! Izanami! Come back! I won't let you die! Don't go! Come back to me, my dear wife!' For a time, he did nothing but cry. For a longer time, he did nothing but stare out to sea at the depths where dolphins and monsters wallowed. For even longer, he tore his hair and ripped his clothes, sang dismal songs and howled. Then he dried his face on his sleeve and went to rescue his poor, lost, little wife, leaping all the way down to the spirit Land of Yomi.

"It was dark there and evil-smelling – a hollow valley, sticky underfoot like the broken shell of a rotten egg. He would never have found his way at all but for his magic comb. Each tooth, plucked from the comb like a match from a book of matches, would burn for a few dazzling seconds. They lit up astonished, ghostly faces, blinking eyes. Suddenly the flame between his fingers was blown out, and a familiar voice spoke out of the darkness. 'Oh Izanagi! Why didn't you come before? I waited! I hoped! I thought, 'He'll never leave me in this dreadful place! But then when you didn't come … '

"'I've come for you now, my love,' said Izanagi.

11

"'Too late! I've already eaten the food cooked in the ovens of Yomi! Now I can never come back to our beautiful island world!' Izanagi went to strike another comb-tooth. He longed to see his wife's beautiful face again. But she begged him: 'No! Don't look at me! I've already started to change. Remember me as I was!'

"'Change? How change?' The flame flared up.

"The sight that confronted Izanagi made him drop the comb-tooth. It continued to burn on the ground, lighting up what he did not want to see. Izanami's huge, slug-white body was entwined with rumbling, grumbling, grinning monsters. Izanagi clapped his hand to his mouth, heaved up his heart and turned to run.

"'How could you, husband! How could you shame me so! Now I can never let you leave here to tell the world what I've become!' She and her friends lumbered after him – gigantic, hideous, heaving mounds of blubber like giant seals, barking and reeking, snatching and reaching.

"Izanagi threw down the wreath of grapes and vine leaves from round his head. All but Izanami stopped to squabble over the grapes and wolf them down. Izanami gained on him and cut him off by the cave-doors of Yomi.

"'Get off! Let me go! I can't bear to look at you! I divorce you, you hear? I divorce you! You're no wife of mine any more!'

"The fat face, all hung about with ratted, matted hair, smiled sweetly at him. 'Oh beloved, don't! Because if you do, I'll be forced to strangle all those little people we made, you and I.'

"*Then I'll just have to create them all over again, shan't I?*' retorted Izanagi. He rushed out of the Land of Yomi, straight into the ocean. There he washed the smell from his hands and the slime from his hair, and wept tears saltier than the salt sea.

"Every tear that fell on to the breaking surf became a god. From his right eye he wept a daughter with so bright a smile that the world gasped in wonder. Her father sent her up the spear-ladder, to light both Heaven and Earth with her smile. From his left eye he wept a son – more pale and less warm than his sister, but almost as handsome. He sent Moon up the spear-ladder, too, to light the opposite end of the sky from his sister, Sun.

"Izanagi wept eight million gods in his grief. Then he crept away to the ends of the Earth, to a beach where the turtles lay their soft, secret eggs. He lived there alone with his memories while, far away, the people he and Izanami had made grew and thrived, loved and died, beneath the Rainbow Bridge."

"A splendid story, thank you," said the cleric politely. "For a few minutes, it quite took our minds off our predicament."

"Yes, but why couldn't she tell it right?" demanded the Viking, who had become increasingly baffled as the story unfolded. "That's not the way the world began. You can't meddle with those kind of stories. They're sacred. They have to be told right."

"Then tell it as it should be," said the Japanese girl, without resentment. "It will help us pass the time."

"I don't want to pass the time!" raged the Viking. "I want to do something! Signal someone. Look for land. Row. Fish. At least let's fish!"

So they fished, with feathers from the Maori's belt, and posted someone to keep watch for a sail, a headland, a sign. But they still wanted the Viking to tell a story for fear he might otherwise throw everything off the raft but the one egg.

CHAPTER 3
The cow and the giant

"At the centre was a hole, a pit, a nothingness: Ginnungagap. To the North were icy fogs and streams of poisonous cold, and to the South, fields of fire. The freezing streams spilled over the brink of Ginnungagap and filled it with glaciers of poisonous ice. Ice and fire. Fire and ice. For aeons they chafed and clashed, like sword on shield, until the sparks flew up one day over the brink of Ginnungagap and took shape where they landed.

"What shapes they took! A huge man and a huger cow, with only each other for company. Ymir the Giant lay beneath the cow each day and milked her, squirting the white milk directly into his cavernous mouth. Those jets of milk pouring into Ymir's mouth were like the streams of ice filling Ginnungagap but good, wholesome and rich. When he was not drinking, he slept. He was a creature so ugly that even the cow rarely turned her head in his direction.

"While Ymir drank and slept, the cow licked the salty, ice-slippery rim of Ginnungagap, staring down into the depths with doleful, brown eyes. Her great tongue rasped over the stones until, after a million years or so, the stones were quite worn down.

"One day, while Ymir lay snoring, the cow's tongue licked something hairy and warm – the curly top of a man's head. Soon she had laid bare face and chest, arms and legs, and up sprang Buri as if woken by the licking of his dog. He was as handsome as Ymir was ugly, and smaller, too – more like you and me. He crossed to where the sleeping giant lay, milky-mouthed beneath the cow.

"Ymir did not wake but all of a sudden his body began to stir. From out of his hairy ears, his flaring nostrils, his lolling mouth, his armpits crept gruesome, little children who grew, instantly into a brotherhood of giants. Their heads were stone, their shoulders like boulders, their hands and feet carved from ice and their beards were needles of frost. Some changed into eagles and swooped about the sunless, moonless Overhead. Some howled themselves into wolves. The rest snarled and sneered about them, hunched and punching, ready for a fight. They kicked the cosmic cow and smashed the ice with their fists. They hurled icicle-daggers into Ginnungagap just to hear the echo. They were foul-mouthed and rough, swaggering and crude, and their breath froze in the air like bird droppings. Last of all, from under the arches of Ymir's feet emerged a hideous, six-headed troll.

"'I'd like a son, too,' thought Buri, 'but preferably not like any of these.' Just then, from out of Ymir's cupped and sleeping hands, and from under his eyelids, came female giants – more attractive than the males by far, with their rain-dark hair and snow-white skin. Indeed, one was so fair that Buri took note of her name – Bestla – and married her. From this handsome couple came the first gods – such a race as was to fill Heaven with stories enough for a thousand firelit nights.

"The children of Ymir – those frost giants – grew up unruly and coarse, throwing insults and punches and rocks all day long. War soon broke out between the sons of Buri and the sons of Ymir – though all the while Ymir, the father-giant, slept on in the shadow of the cosmic cow. In fact, the frost-giants used the sleeping Ymir as their citadel, crouching behind his legs, catapulting ice-blocks over his nose, leaping on his spongy stomach to shout oaths at the enemy. The gods stormed their citadel, scaling Ymir's arms, setting fire to his hair. Finally, they opened a wound so deep that the blood leapt out like water through a breached dam. It sluiced away whole ranks of frost-giants; swept them quite away. It washed away the camp where the womenfolk sat cooking. It drowned their stone-headed, hooligan children. Only one frost-giant, Bergelmir, escaped with his wife, jumping into a hollow treetrunk and floating away over rapids of foaming blood in the world's very first canoe.

"Odin, Vili and Ve, chief among the sons of Buri, took hold of Ymir's feet and dragged the body to the brink of Ginnungagap's yawning chasm. Perhaps they intended to roll it over into the poisonous icepit below. But as they dragged him along, they noticed how his spilt blood puddled and pooled into lakes and tarns of fresh water. Alive, Ymir had done nothing but drink and sleep; maybe dead he could be of more use.

"So out of his flesh the triumphant gods made soil – a layer deep enough to cover the flat, icy ground. From his bones they made mountains. From the unburned locks of his hair they made trees curly with leaves, tendrilled vines and beans. Heaving his massive skull into the air, they appointed four dwarfs – Northman, Southman, Eastman and Westman – to hold it up high for ever. When they slung Ymir's brains upwards, too, they tattered into clouds and drifted about without falling back to Earth.

"It was hard to see their finished handiwork in the dark, so the gods travelled south to the Land of Fire. There they captured, like leaping salmon, enough sparks to make sun, moon and stars. They lit the place they had made and called it 'Midgard' or 'Middle Earth', because it stood between the lands of Fire and Ice."

"Well, of course, your kind of people would come up with that kind of myth," said the scientist. "Ice, fjords, cold, volcanoes, foul weather … They'd all give rise to violent, brutal myths – giants, trolls, all that … Very understandable in a primitive culture living in a harsh landscape."

The Viking lumbered across the raft like a frost-giant and seized him by the throat. "You calling me a liar?" The others tried to restrain him, but his strength was immense. His face twisted into a troll's grimace. "You saying I got it wrong?"

"Not at all, not … at all!" croaked the scientist. As the Viking bent him over the side of the raft, his hair trailed in the water, his ears filled up, the waves washed over his face. He felt like Ymir poised on the brink of Ginnungagap. "An excellent account, excellent … " he gasped.

The Viking relented and sat down, scowling out from between his hairy knees.

"That wasn't the first canoe!" said the Maori.

"And I say it was. You see something wrong with my story?" The Viking slammed the words down like a challenge: one storyteller recognising a rival.

"The first canoe came down in the first egg," claimed the Maori. That word again. The travellers shifted unhappily. No one was hungry yet, but what else was there to think about but that one brown egg among fifteen mouths?

"I believe we should *all* listen to each other with patience and tolerance," said the clerical gentleman coyly. "There's certainly something about these surroundings which puts one in mind of – ah – Day One. I daresay we each have a *slightly* different notion of how the world began, and it would be most interesting to hear your different – ah – quaint tales. And won't it pass the time splendidly until we are picked up? Only a matter of time, I do assure you, ladies. Simply a matter of time."

Time did pass, like a ship on the horizon, too distant to see them and turn aside from its course; moving too fast to stop.

CHAPTER 4

The battle of land, sea and storm

"Once there were only night, day, space and a great, single sea. Nothing lived on the sea or under it. Something must have lived overhead, though, for one day an egg dropped down and broke as it hit the water. Out of it came a man, a woman, a dog, a pig and a canoe. The man and woman climbed into the canoe, pulled the dog and pig aboard, then paddled away through day and night, over the single sea until the boat ran aground.

"The boat was not small. For that boat was the first country. My country. Oh yes, now it is a chain of islands, I know, but once it was a single stretch of land, bare and flat and vast. The man's name was Rangi and the woman's name was Papa, and they loved each other very, very much.

"In fact they were always touching, always kissing, always held in each other's arms. All day, all night and all year they clung, skin against skin, mouth against mouth, palm against palm, cheek against chest – so close that not a ray of light could pass between them.

"Many children, all boys, were conceived in Papa's womb thanks to this great love but, because the embrace was endless, there was no chance, no room, no time for them to be born. The children grew to quite an age inside their mother's womb. They grew into men, in fact, and they argued, as brothers will.

"They quarrelled, they argued, they wrestled and cursed one another. Being cooped up together made it worse. The one thing they *all* wanted was *to get out* of Papa's womb. They pushed and they shouted, they hammered and they yelled, but Rangi and

Papa clung as close as ever.

"'Let's kill them both and be done with it!' snarled Enga (who was a brawling, violent kind of boy).

"'No, no,' said Mahuta. 'Give me a chance first to get us out of here.' So he finally squeezed himself between mother and father and, putting his hands and head against his mother's stomach, planted his feet against his father's chest and pushed for all he was worth. His back arched, his legs strained, the blood vessels stood proud in his neck. At last their father Rangi was forced apart from his beloved wife – up into the sky where he stayed – Sky God Rangi, alone, above.

"Mahuta stood tall on the Earth, as tall as the trees he planted to keep the sky away, as gentle as the creatures he made to live in his forests: monkeys and birds and men of peace. Enga, on the other hand, created fearsome men of war.

"Most of the brothers decided to stay with their mother and forget their father, but Whiri felt a greater closeness to his father. Being a wild, wayward and whirling boy, he went to live with Rangi, who made him God of the Storm and gave him powers enough to kill his 'treacherous' brothers.

"Whiri loosed an attack against Papa and her sons so fierce that they reeled under it. Storms and lightning, in turn, blackened the sky and rent it apart with fire. Hurricanes lashed the forests of Mahuta, felling trees and flattening every palm-leaf house. Tidal waves came towering ashore – great running walls of glassy water. Rain as black as pitch beat down on gods, man and animal alike, until their knees buckled and they staggered in slurrying mud.

"Only Enga the Fierce One, and the race of fierce people he had made, stood up to the Storm God. With catapults and stones, fists and sharpened bones, spears and the horns of wild beasts, they fought him off. At last the Storm God withdrew, having smashed the single island into pieces so far apart that canoes might never travel the distance from one fragment to the next.

"When Enga had finally beaten off the enemy, he turned on his lesser brothers in disgust. 'A lot of use *you* were, you bunch of cowards! You worthless rabble!' He took hold of his little brother Tangaroa with both fists. 'You wouldn't even fight, you squirt! You're obviously in league with Whiri and Rangi! Well, get out there and keep them company!' And he threw Tangaroa off the land and far out to sea.

"Tangaroa was obliged to make his home there, in halls of deepest blue. He cruised the oceans until he came to the island home of Faumea, a sorceress, and married her. Their first children were the fish of the world, and the turtles, the urchins and squid, the seahorses, watersnakes, plankton and jellyfish. (Not everything that lived in the cellars of the sea was born of Tangaroa, however, nor obeyed his commands. Demons lurked in the dark sea caves – demons like Rogo the Octopus, who answered to no one.)

"After throwing out Tangaroa, the ferocious Enga turned on Mahuta. But gentle Mahuta soothed him with soft words and presents – presents made from the wood of his forests: canoes and wooden fish-hooks, houses and throwing spears. And so, the fierce people and the gentle ones settled down and managed to live together, tolerant of each others' differences.

"Meanwhile, the outcast Tangaroa and his sorceress wife had a human son, Turi, who married a lovely girl called Hina, to everyone's great joy.

"Young Turi and Hina liked to surf each morning, riding the

curling waves on shining palm leaves of glossy green. Further and further they waded out to catch the perfect wave, the longest ride: beyond the fourth wave, the fifth, the sixth …

"One morning, Hina ventured beyond the seventh wave. Just as she jumped to board her palm leaf, a black tentacle reached out of the wave and grasped her about the waist. 'Turi! Turi! Save me!' she screamed, before the water closed over her head.

"Turi was frantic with grief. He ran to his father for help. Together they built a canoe, hollowing out a tree with axes and fire. Faumea the sorceress gave them magic, multi-coloured feathers, and these they tied to wooden fish-hooks for bait. Then they paddled their canoe out to sea until they were riding right over the sea-cave of Rogo. The water there was black, as though with the ink of squid, and there was not a seabird in sight.

"Turi and Tangaroa let down their hooks. The canoe all but capsized as some monstrous mouth far below seized the magic feathers. Muscles straining, teeth clenched, backs flexed, son and father hauled on the line. It cut their fingers, it bit deep into the side of the canoe, but little by little they reeled in the fish-line and the gruesome body knotted to its end. Eight tentacles waved above the water, grasped them about the neck and slapped them in the face. With his axe Tangaroa cut off the tentacles one by one until nothing but head, eye and mouth remained. And from the mouth they pulled Hina.

"Although Tangaroa killed the demon octopus, his other fishy sons and daughters are very dear to him. He takes it amiss when we sons of Enga and Mahuta fish the ocean with hooks. Now and then he takes his revenge, pulling a canoe under, drowning the beaches with a freak tide, or nibbling on the coastline; nibbling, nibbling, nibbling away at our island world."

"But that's exactly what the Ancient Greeks believed!" exclaimed the clergyman, eyeing the Maori suspiciously as if he might have stolen the story while no one was looking. "Mother and father clinging too close to let their children be born … And then one of the sons forcing his way out! What a coincidence! Amazing!"

The Maori seemed to find nothing amazing about it. "It is how the world began," he said. "Why should the truth alter just because it is spoken long ago or ten thousand miles away?"

CHAPTER 5
Six-day wonder

The vicar had a look of profound sorrow on his face. "Oh dear, oh dear!" At last he got to his feet, moaning a little. He was not a good sailor, and the skin alongside his mutton-chop whiskers was as green as mint sauce.

The Maori looked up at him expectantly. "Quiet! The old man is going to tell us his story!"

But the old man did not seem to be finding speech easy. "I'm afraid ... I'm sorry to say ... ," he began. "I regret to tell you ... that you're ... well ... all wrong."

"Oh I know it's not your fault," he added quickly. "I don't suppose you've had the chance – well, I'm sure some of you haven't ... to read the Holy Bible."

The scientist made a noise like a punctured tyre. "You're never going to give us that old thing! The fig-leaves and the snake?"

The vicar ignored him. "Please don't take offence," he said to the others, fiddling with his shirtcuffs, "but you see ... in the beginning was the Word."

A blank look passed around the raft. "Which word?" inquired the lady with almond eyes politely.

"To put it another way ... " said the vicar, his cheeks colouring deeply. "God said, *Before the world was, I am.*"

"Precisely," agreed the Egyptian. "Just as I shall tell you. 'Kephera said: there was no one other than me. Alone I did it.'"

The vicar closed his eyes and plunged on with his story.

"The Book of Genesis tells us how, in the beginning, the Earth was shapeless and empty and – ah – wet. And on the first day, the Lord Almighty moved over the surface of the water and said, 'Let there be light' – and so there was!

"Next day, He created the sky – that's to say, the Earth's atmosphere.

"On the third, He separated dry land from the seas and planted the land with grass and trees and herbs and bushes and flowers. When it was finished, He liked what He had done. It was good.

"Next day, He set the sun and the moon in the sky: that's to say, He began the notion of Time passing – when it is winter, when it is summer, when the days are longest and shortest and when the tides ebb and flow. At first there were no rainclouds to water the growing things on the Earth, but soon the heat of the sun drew up a great mist out of the sodden ground, and filled the clouds with sweet, welcome rain.

"After that, on the fifth day, He said, 'Let the seas and skies be filled with living things – whales and fishes and birds and bats. Let them all know, from the very start, how to mate and breed, so that from two will come ten and from ten, hundreds and from hundreds, millions.' Soon there were birds perching in every tree and on the ledges of every cliff, and the oceans were rainbow-coloured with shoals of countless fish, and whales moved through the waves, themselves as huge as islands.

"On the sixth day, God made everything else – insects, cattle, reptiles, amphibians, mammals … And they all knew instinctively how to mate and breed, so that a single family of wildebeest quickly grew into a herd stretching from horizon to horizon. A pair of ants soon set a whole forest a-swarm with life.

"All those species: aardvarks and manatees, tortoises and

honey bees … and still there was time before nightfall for the greatest creation of all. God decided to set a master over the animals – someone to care for them. 'Let us make Man,' He said."

"Us?" said the Egyptian. "Did the animals help him, then?"

"No, no," said the vicar, flustered. "He was speaking to the angels."

"Why, when did he create them? You didn't say anything about angels," said the Muslim.

"No, well, they existed before Time itself, you see. They always were. They never weren't. It's very complicated. And besides, He may have been speaking to His son."

"So he *wasn't* all alone, then, in making the world! You said he was all alone."

"Yes, yes, He was. There are three different aspects to God: the Father, the Son and the Holy Spirit. You may have heard of the Son. He finally came down to Earth in the shape of an ordinary man. That was Jesus Christ … It's my fault. I'm not explaining it very well. Look at it this way: in one lifetime you may well be a child to your parents, a parent to your children, a husband to your wife, a friend to someone else! It doesn't make you more than one person, does it?"

The Egyptian leaned forward and patted the vicar consolingly. "I understand you perfectly. Your god, he is like our God of the Storm whose four faces look to the four corners of the Earth."

The vicar's face twitched with horror and he plunged headlong back into the story.

"'Let us make Man like us, an intelligent creature, who can love and imagine and understand!' So, on the sixth day, God moulded a handful of earth into the shape of a man, and blew the breath of life into his nostrils. He gave Man the world for a present. 'Take care of it, Adam. I am making you Lord of all Creation. Into your care I entrust the fish and animals, the trees and crops. Help yourself to the fruit and berries. Harvest all the grain and herbs and vegetables you need: they are your food. Everything you need, I have provided. And it is all very good, you must agree.' The Sun was just then setting on the sixth day.

"On the seventh, God rested from making the world. 'You must stop work, too, and rest on the seventh day of each week,' he told Adam. 'A holy day to refresh yourself in body and mind.'

"Adam's home was a garden planted specially for him in the East, a land bordered by three rivers and planted with everything necessary for a wonderful life. Paradise. We would be living there now, if Adam and his wife had behaved themselves … "

CHAPTER 6
Paradise lost

"Yes! Yes! This is all true! This is the story of how Allah made first man and first woman!"

The vicar seemed put out to have the Muslim agree with him. "This is the word of the *Christian* Bible, sir!" he said.

"And the Jewish," said the scientist.

"Of course, yes, naturally, the Jewish," admitted the vicar.

"And the truth as told to the prophet Muhammad by the Angel Gabriel!" exclaimed the Muslim happily, and he took over the story.

"To be precise, Allah made Adam out of seven colours of soil. The angels brought them to him from the different regions of his Earth – some fertile, some barren, some hot and dry, some cool and moist. After that, as the elderly gentleman told you, Allah did indeed breathe life into the man he had made, and planted a garden for him to live in and to tend.

"Then he saw that Adam was lonely. So while the man slept, Allah opened his side and took out a rib – the last and lowest rib – and made from it a woman, a friend, a soul-mate for Adam. In the garden at Eden they were able to live, safe and quiet. We have a word in Arabic: *asalam*. It means being safe and at rest, obedient to the will of Allah, knowing that His ways are the best.

"Now in the garden were all manner of orchards and bushes bearing fruits as sweet as happiness. 'You may eat fruit from every tree in the garden except one,' said Allah. 'In the middle of

Eden stands the Tree of the Knowledge of Good and Evil. Don't ever eat from that; if you do, it will put an end to your life here.'

"For a long time, Adam and Eve lived happily – as carefree as children among the blossoms of Eden's orchards. There was no need for heavy digging or weeding: the garden was so fertile that the branches bent and the grain stooped under the weight of its harvest – ripe for the picking. The weather was always warm, never too hot. Husband and wife ran about as naked as the other animals. What need of clothes?

"But Eve was intrigued by the tree at the centre of the garden. Time and time again she returned to look at it. One day, coiled round the trunk like ivy, a snake beckoned to her with a wave of its emerald head. Not a snake perhaps, so much as a lizard, for it had legs which raised it up off the ground and a proud, erect head. It was very beautiful.

"'Eat from this-s-s tree, why don't you?' said the lizard.

"'Allah said we must never eat the fruit of the Tree of the Knowledge of Good and Evil,' said Eve. 'If we do, we will die.'

"'Die? Never! He just wants-s-s you to think s-so. He doesn't want you to eat from the tree, because He likes you to remain ignorant. It's fruit would make you wise like Him, powerful like Him, on a par in every way with Him and the angels-s-s! Eat. Eat. And if you love Adam, s-save s-some for him.' People have called that snake Satan or the Devil, Tempter, Deceiver or Fallen Angel. But he did not force Eve to eat, nor Adam to taste the forbidden fruit. They both had the choice – to obey Allah or not.

"No sooner had they swallowed a mouthful of the delicious fruit than a thousand thoughts came swirling into their heads. A part of the brain that had always been empty, cheerful, light, was suddenly filled with ideas: cruelty and deceit, jealousy and greed, rudeness and spite, anger and sadness. They looked down at their beautiful, sunburned bodies made by the very hands of God, and saw only nakedness, indecency. So they rushed to make loincloths by sewing together the big, glossy leaves of the fig tree. While they sewed, they bickered and quarrelled, cursed and blushed. Before the silly aprons were made, Allah came walking among the cool, evening shadows of the garden, calling out to them by name. 'He mustn't see us like this!' cried Eve. 'Quick! Hide in the bushes!'

"Allah came straight to them, of course, and asked why they had tried to hide themselves away. 'We were ashamed to be seen like this – you know, stark naked.'

"'Who told you you were naked?' Allah demanded.

"'She made me eat it! Eve made me!' whined Adam, but it was too late for excuses. God drove them both out of Eden – out into a land strewn with rocks and weeds. 'From now on you must work if you want to eat – plough, sow, weed, reap and store; struggle against weather and disaster; cry and sweat; ache and worry. Even your children will give you pain when they are born and pain as they grow, disappointing you as you have disappointed me.' And He posted an angel at the gate of Eden with a flailing, three-edged, blazing sword, to keep humans out of Paradise.

"As for the snake, Allah condemned it to crawl forever on its belly and taste nothing but ash between its jaws. And because Allah has only to speak for his wishes to be carried out, the snake does crawl, and Eden is lost to us for ever.

"There is only one way for men and women to glimpse the peace and happiness of those first innocent days: and that is to obey the

laws of Allah. That's why I must say my prayers now," said the Muslim, breaking off abruptly, and trying to judge the time of day by the position of the sun. "Does anyone happen to know in which direction is the holy city of Mecca?"

Instead of answering, the scientist said, "Yes, it's always the women who get blamed for the rotten state of the world. I suppose men like it that way, so that's the way they tell it."

CHAPTER 7

No going back

"That's right, that's right," said a sun-shrivelled man in the centre of the raft, wagging a finger at the sky. "If it weren't for women we should all be in Heaven now! Perfectly true."

"Where are you from?" asked the women, in chorus.

"From the Warau, of course," he said, and they managed to deduce he was from Guiana in Central America. The Warau man explained why women were to blame for all his troubles.

"Our Maker, Kononatee, meant us all to live in Heaven with him. If he said so today, I know I'd be content to live there. But the young people – you know what young people are – they wanted to travel. A hunter found a hole in the sky one day, and down he went to see what he could see, shoot what he could shoot. Everyone followed him. Silly sheep, following without a thought. And Kononatee let them go. 'Just so long as you don't go near the Lake of Magic Secrets,' he said. 'That would not be wise.'

"Down on Earth they looked about, didn't like what they found and decided to go back. But why did they let a woman go first? And if so, why Fat Anna? She got her arms through, she pushed through her head. She squeezed and squirmed. The people behind pushed with all their might. When they saw it was no good, they tried to pull her out again. But she was stuck fast, blocking the route back to Heaven.

"The people scratched their heads. 'Kononatee Our Maker will make a fresh hole for us.' So they sat on the Earth and waited. The day was hot, the flies buzzed, the ants bit and the dust got into their mouths, ears and eyes. The sweat trickling down felt like crawling insects, too. 'I don't know why we bothered to come to such a nasty place,' muttered the visitors, while high above them Fat Anna kept up a muffled din: *'Pull me out, can't you? Or push me through! Don't just leave me here! The sun's hot on my head! The sky's squeezing my lunch! I've got an itch I can't scratch!'*

"Kononatee seemed to be taking a very long time to make a new hole. Two bored maidens plucked at their dresses, peeling the cotton off their sweat-wet skin. 'I need a bath,' said Winnie.

"'A cool swim,' said Minnie, 'in that lake.'

"'That's the Lake of Magic Secrets,' said Winnie nervously. 'Kononatee told us not to … '

"'I wonder what's secret about it.'

"'Something he doesn't want us to know, maybe?'

"'Guilty secrets, you mean?'

"'Or the source of his magic powers,' whispered Winnie.

"They slipped away from the others and went down to the lake, through the mud to where the lake was fringed with pink crayfish and glistening caddis. The water broke round their ankles, round their knees, then swirled their dresses as they swam lazily out to the lake's turquoise centre. From the sky, Kononatee saw how they had disobeyed him.

"The water-monsters living at the bottom of the lake also saw the swimmers. With a squirm and a scuttle, they left their dark lair, pumping upwards into the daylit water. With black, suckered tentacles they snatched Minnie and Winnie and drew them down again into the airless dark – to be their unwilling wives.

"'Kononatee! Kononatee! May we come back now?' called the men.

"'Why ask me?'

"'Because Fat Anna is stuck in the hole and we need you to make a new way into Heaven!'

"'Then you should have respected my word while you were on Earth, instead of letting Minnie and Winnie swim in the Magic Lake.'

"'Well, we're sorry about that, but … '

"'Not half as sorry as Winnie and Minnie.'

"'But *we* didn't do anything! Not *us men*. Let us in, Kononatee! This Earth is full of ants and fever and thorn trees and snakes.'

"'The snakes are the children of Winnie and Minnie,' replied the Maker. 'If people will marry water-monsters, what other sort of children can they hope for? At least the water-snakes will stop you ever again daring to swim in the forbidden lakes of Earth.'

"They called out again, and went on calling, but no one answered. For Kononatee had gone to the far end of the sky, and the only sound from above was the grunting of Fat Anna plugging the sky. That's why we people of the Warau *never* go swimming."

CHAPTER 8

Hope on a rope

"Not at all! Rubbish! On the contrary, we owe it all to a woman! Our lands, our pastures, our cows … "

"Not more cows," said the scientist with a world-weary sneer.

"And what's so comical about cows?" demanded the Bantu, bristling with indignation. "Myself I have thirty. It's my guess, sir, you have none at all, or you would not belittle cows."

The assembly turned to look at the scientist. It was true: he hadn't a cow to his name. "No cows! I admit it!" he jeered.

"Then you are a man of little worth, and you will please keep a respectful silence while I tell the true history of the world. Your fellow-countryman is right. The world did take six days to make, but it was no paradise when it was finished. No!"

"On the first day of creation, Wele, the Giver-out, raised Heaven over the Earth, propping it up with pillars just as the roof of a round-hut is propped. He made two big, shiny fellows next, to light up the world: Brother Moon and Brother Sun.

"Like two monkeys on a single branch, the brothers sat there at first, both as bright as each other. But since when could brothers ever sit still and peaceable? No sooner did Wele turn his back than young Moon pushed his younger brother Sun off the perch and toppled him down to the ground. Like a big orange melon – splat in the mud.

"Up jumped Sun, wiped himself clean and scrambled aloft again. He took Moon by an arm and a leg and slung him down –

and even when Moon was lying in the mud, his younger brother came and kicked mud over him, splashing it in his face.

"'Stop! Peace! Stop your fighting this instant!' stormed the Giver-out when he saw them brawling. 'Since you can't live peaceably, I'll shut you in different lofts of Heaven.' And so he did. From then on, Sun shone during the day and Moon shone at night – except that his shine was all slubbered over with mud and his face dirtied. That's why night is so much darker than day.

"Next, Wele made clouds, and the cockerel Lightning who cackles from cloud to cloud. He made stars and rain and the rainbow which stops the rain. He made the two kinds of air: the warm kind full of grass-seed; the other cold kind seeded with hailstones. Two days it took him to make all this, and Brother Sun gave him the light to work by. But as for warmth, Sun kept that to himself, keeping his rays curled up, secret, never thinking to share them.

"Wele made Mwambu and Sela – First Man and First Woman – and set them down on the Earth. He stocked the land all about them with good things – animals, trees, fish and insects (although they did not prosper very well because of the cold).

"It wasn't Wele who made the monsters: they must have been there already. Mwambu and Sela could hear the monsters at night, roaming about, hunting through the trees, flattening the grass with their big feet and roaring horribly. So the house they built was raised up on stilts, out of reach of the monsters.

"In six days the world was finished. Thanks to the Sun, Mwambu could see his wife Sela, see the ground to farm it, see the cows to count them. But the grass did not grow lush where the few cows grazed, the cows did not grow fat, nor did Mwambu."

"In their little hut on stilts, Mwambu and Sela had many children – brave sons and beautiful daughters, brave daughters and beautiful sons, and their children in turn had children. There was no room for such a big family to live in the little round-hut, so the bravest of the children made themselves spears and said, 'Let's be rid of these monsters so that we can sleep on the ground and build our houses where we like.'

"They trapped the beasts in tar-pits, drowned them in lakes, and left their giant bones and sabre teeth strewing the African countryside. So the children and grandchildren of Mwambu and Sela slept on the ground and built many, many houses without stilts. Boys from one village married girls from another, celebrating with the roasting of a cow, as custom demanded. But such marriages cost their parents dear, for the cows in the fields were so few.

"Abala's father, for example, had only one sorry cow. But he would gladly have slaughtered it to see his daughter married. She was as beautiful as a star-powdered sky, as slender as a willow, as strong as sisal. The sound of her singing, as she fed the scrawny chickens, made the deer swivel their ears, the termites stir in the earth. But she would not marry.

"Every boy in her own village wanted to marry her. Boys in every other village wanted to marry her. But Abala would have none of them. 'I am waiting,' she said, 'for he who is meant for me.'

"One chilly noon, while Abala milked her father's only cow, a rope came snaking down out of Heaven – *crack!* – like a whip. It startled the cow so much that she trotted away. Some girls might have trotted away as well, but not Abala. She walked round the rope and fingered its fraying end. Then she took hold with both hands and it lifted her off the ground.

"Up she went, past the pale, bald treetops, past the stringy clouds, past the birds fluffed up against the cold. At last she reached a round-hut rather like her own, but seventy times as big. An old lady greeted her and helped her climb indoors. 'I am sorry to disturb your milking, my dear,' she said, 'but my son happened to pass by your house recently and saw you feeding the chickens. He has formed a great fancy to marry you.'

"'I am honoured,' said Abala. 'But who exactly is your son?'

"'Why the Sun, of course, child!'

"It was a surprise – one moment to be milking a cow, the next to be standing in the house of the Sun. But Abala simply leaned her head to one side and said, 'I'll hear what he has to say.'

"Just then, the Sun came home and took Abala walking in the gardens of Heaven. Looking around, she saw big-petalled flowers the colour of sunset, fountains of glittering rainwater, arbours of birdsong and herds of chestnut cows – fat, glossy and full of milk. The sun offered her the wedding present of a huge, earthenware pot. When she peeped inside, she saw that the pot contained the Sun's rays, all coiled up like ribbons. They were so bright that her eyes were dazzled, so hot that the pot was as hot as any cooking pot freshly taken out of the fire.

"'I shall marry you, my lord Sun,' said Abala. 'For I see now that you are the husband I have been waiting for. I think we shall be very happy.'

"So they were. Abala bore three sons in three years, and spent her days playing with them in the gardens, and milking the numberless cows of Heaven. At the end of three years she said to her husband, as they lay together beneath a bedspread of cloud, 'Let me go and visit my family. It's so long since I've seen them, and I left with no time to say goodbye. Please let me go.'

"Grudgingly the Sun agreed: 'As long as you come back soon.'

"Abala's mother-in-law lowered her down on the same length of sisal rope – to the very edge of Abala's village (much to the surprise of her father's only cow).

"Now, after Abala climbed the rope to Heaven, her family had searched for her in vain. They thought wild animals must have killed and eaten her. So when her father and mother saw her standing there, shivering in the chilly sunlight, they burst into tears of joy. 'Kill the cow! We'll feast and dance and sing, because our beautiful daughter is not dead but married and come back to visit us! Even though she's a grand lady now, living in Heaven with a lordly husband, she remembered her old parents and came home to visit them! Kill the cow and roast it!'

"'But father, you only have one cow!' said Abala in distress. 'What will become of you if you kill it in honour of me?'

"'Let come what comes,' said her father, dancing with uncontainable joy. 'It is the custom and the custom must be kept. My daughter is married and has three fine sons, and still in her happiness she did not forget us!' The whole village was happy, but Abala could not help comparing Earth with Heaven. Down here everything was so dismal and comfortless.

"At the end of the week she kissed her parents goodbye, walked to the edge of the village and found the rope hanging down from the sky. Her family waved until she was out of sight. Then they turned sadly homewards, wondering how they would live without even one scrawny cow to give them milk.

"As soon as Abala reached home, she went to the corner of the big hut and found the earthenware jar. She carried it to the doorway, lifted off the lid and tipped it over, so that the contents spilled out. Like the ribbons from a sewing-basket, like the carpets from a merchant's overturned cart, the Sun's golden rays unfurled out of Heaven, fluttering a little on the breeze.

"When the pot was empty, Abala took a stick and went outdoors. She flicked the rumps of thirty fat, idle cows and stampeded them through a hole in the clouds. They fell with the lightness of rain – a hailstorm of cows – and when they touched the ground, sat down until they got over the shock. The villagers ran out to stare at the cows in their yards and in their fields. The cows stared back with large, mournful eyes. Suddenly both cow and villager felt the warm sunlight falling on their backs.

"The yellow pasture started to turn green; the trees came into blossom. Flies droned through the hot air and the grain ripened at the tips of the long grass. 'Even in Heaven our daughter thinks of us,' said Abala's father, beaming almost as brightly as the Sun's rays.

"At first the Sun himself was annoyed with Abala for giving away the precious contents of the earthenware pot.

"'Weren't they my present?' she asked him. 'Weren't they mine to do with as I saw fit?'

"Then the Sun looked down at the Earth and saw how it was changing in the warmth. He saw people look up at Heaven with smiling faces and call out blessings and praise on Abala and her lordly husband. He decided not to reef in the yellow ribbons and runners of sunshine. 'How good of me to share my wealth with the poor,' he would say from time to time, and Abala would reply, 'Yes, my dear. How good.' Then she would catch the eye of her mother-in-law, wink and smile and go on milking the numberless cows of Heaven."

CHAPTER 9
A big mistake

"If the first two people *had* been a man and a woman, we might be better off than we are!" complained a woman of dark-skin and tightly crinkled hair. She said she was from Britain, which confused everyone. As her story progressed, it became clear she was not from the island of *Great* Britain, but the much smaller, far more exotic island of *New* Britain, half a world away.

"Yes, The-One-Who-Came-First should have made a man and a woman. But we all make mistakes. He made To-Karvuvu; that was his.

"He drew two man-shapes on the ground, bit into his own arm and let the blood fall on to the two figures. Then he covered them with leaves and left them to 'prove' – like a baker does with bread dough. One day, the leaves stirred, a hand, a foot poked out, and there were the first men: To-Kabinana and To-Karvuvu. For you, I shall call them Nana and Vuvu.

"Now Nana was perfect in every way. He had good sense in his head, grace in his body and was full of good ideas.

"One day, Nana climbed a coconut palm, examined the fruits until he found three perfect coconuts, then dropped them carefully to earth on to their pointed ends. As each one hit the ground, it split open and out jumped a girl as beautiful as an orchid. Their natures were as sweet as coconut milk and they made fine wives.

"His brother Vuvu had watched all this, and decided he would get wives for himself the same way. So he climbed the self-same

coconut palm, chose three fruit and dropped them down –
chunk, chunk, chunk. Unfortunately, he had not taken care to
drop them on their pointed ends. They burst open with a splatter
of milk, and out rolled three women so ugly they might have
spent their childhood pushing canoes out to sea with their noses.

"Their natures, too, were as sour and flat as week-old coconut
milk. They led Vuvu a dog's life. Quite often they would throw
him out-of-doors altogether, telling him to 'get out from under
their feet'. Then he would take himself off to the beach and
throw stones at the sea because it did not talk back.

"One day he was doing this when he saw Nana a short way
down the beach, carving a piece of driftwood. He carved a large,
beautiful fish, then waded into the surf with it and set it afloat. At
once the wood came to life and, turning on its tail, thanked Nana
loudly for its life. Then it darted out through the waves to where
other fish lay like silver treasure beneath the sea.

"The fish rounded up lesser fish, as a dog droves sheep, and
ran them ashore – a whole netful of food for Nana's hungry
family.

"'That has to be better than fishing,' said Vuvu to himself, and
scouted about for another piece of wood. 'I shall make my fish
bigger and fiercer, so that it can catch even bigger fish and more
of them,' he thought greedily. He whittled a huge carving, larger
than a man with jagged teeth and long, steely fins.

"When he loosed it into the sea, the magic did not fail him.
The fish came to life – except that it was not like any fish in the
sea, with its three banks of teeth and flexing tail. Its great jaws
gulped down fish with terrifying savagery. It would have eaten
Vuvu too, if he had not beetled out of the water as fast as his legs
would carry him. Vuvu had invented the shark, and the world's

fishermen cursed him for it ever after. The sea was now an even more dangerous place, and they had to share their catches with the ravenous shark.

"That is how it began and that is how it went on: Nana doing things right and Vuvu doing the same things, but doing them wrong. All the men and women of the world are descended from Nana, Vuvu and their coconut wives. Can't you tell? Just when everything seems to be going along marvellously, something happens to knock it all awry.

"The spirit of Vuvu blunders on, you see, making a tragedy out of a triumph, a disaster out of a dream. It was not the intention of He-Who-Came-First, but then he did not foresee how a little stupidity could undo so much cleverness. One thing is for sure: wherever Nana is, his clumsy, bungling twin won't be far away, undoing most of his brother's good work.

"Take this raft," said the New Briton thoughtfully. "'How lucky it was here when we needed it!' you say. But suppose it carries us to the shores of an island full of cannibals. Not so lucky after all, eh?" And with that cheering thought, the Melanesian fell silent. They all shivered with sudden cold.

CHAPTER 10

Snake support

"I don't care what he says about women," said an African lady pointing an accusing finger at the clergyman. "But he ought to mind what he says about snakes. Calling them evil, indeed! Where would you be without snakes, I'd like to know? Where would we all be?

"On the day the world began, Creator called Giant Snake to him and climbed into his mouth. 'Carry me about, friend, and let us make a world out of this wetness.' So though there was nothing but sea just then, Great Snake carried Creator from North to South, East to West. His twisting coils gathered small, floating things and pressed them together into solid land. Meanwhile Creator made mountains and trees, elephants, turtles and cows, and placed them on the land. The more he made, the better he became at making.

"In perfecting his art, Creator made a great many jungles, deserts and plains. Each mountain was bigger and more beautiful than the last, each landscape more picturesque. But in the joy of making, Creator piled just too many things aboard the island Earth. It started to sink under the weight. The mountains were simply too full of gold and precious jewels, the jungles were just too busy with trampling elephants. For a time it seemed as if the whole of Creation might capsize, and everything slip back into the sea.

"Then Creator asked Snake to help him. 'Coil yourself into a circle and lie beneath the world to steady it,' he said.

"So Great Snake slipped silently under the listing world, coiling himself round and round, holding it firm and fast. The Earth no longer rolled about, and the work of Greator was saved. Creator charged a tribe of red monkeys (who lived in the sea already) to keep the Snake fed with his favourite food. So from the mines of the oceans they fetched iron bars, night and day, to keep up the serpent's strength.

"Of course the Snake never stops moving, so that as he swims in a circle, the Earth is turned round and round. That's why the stars appear to move in the sky. But such circlings are smooth. Only rarely does Snake sneeze or cough or writhe in a restless dream. Then the coils are set rippling in his monstrous scaly back, and the Earth above shakes and the ground splits open and mountains crumble and fall. The monkeys swim to fetch more iron and Snake, having turned himself about and about like a dog in its basket, settles once more to a stillness."

"One day, of course, the mines will empty of iron," said the African darkly, looking each of her fellow travellers in the eye.

They could not help but ask, "What will happen then?"

"Snake will have to eat the only thing he can."

They did not want to hear, but they had to ask. "What's that?"

"His own tail, of course! Little by little. Shrinking the circle until he bites himself to nothingness. Then the weight of the hippopotami and the trees and the elephants, the wildebeest and the hills and the towns and so on will be just too great. Away we'll all slide – we Fon of Abomey – and you people, whatever tribe you're of. Down we'll go, back into the swaying sea. The waters will close over all Creator made, and the world will come right round to where it began."

There was a moment's silence while the voyagers felt the raft beneath them ride on numberless fathoms of slipping sea.

Then a Hindu gentleman spoke: "Of course it will," he said, serenely calm at the prospect. "But like a snake with its tail in its mouth, even Creation is a circle. Round it goes for ever. Birth – Preservation – Renewal. Birth – Preservation – Renewal ... "

CHAPTER 11

The three faces of God

The Hindu man saw their faces turn towards him, anticipating another story. "You should seek Truth, not stories," he said. "And you haven't the upbringing to understand the meaning of the stories I might tell. For instance, you must understand that God is three-in-one ... Brahma the Creator, Vishnu the Preserver and Shiva the Destroyer."

"You want stories of the world's beginning. Which beginning? There have been so many. Each time, the world returns to nothingness and is re-created.

"It is said that, originally, the essence of life – Brahman planted a seed in the primeval ocean. From the seed grew a golden egg. From the egg hatched Brahma, god of Creation. From the remains of the broken shell, he summoned eight elephants and sent them to the eight compass points of the world, to hold up the sky.

"Then he made the gods, to take charge of each aspect of life: Agni the fire god whom he made from a lotus flower, Surya the sun god with his copper body, and Surya's wife the dawn. King over them all was Indra, god of thunder and lightning. When his work was finished, Brahma rested. The world existed. All that remained was to preserve it from its enemies.

"If it is stories you want, I'll tell you of Vishnu the Preserver, for he has visited the earth twenty-eight times, disguising his beautiful blue features and riding the sun-bird Garada.

"Before the Flood – the last one, I mean, for there have been many – Vishnu took the shape of a tiny fish and allowed himself to be carried to a virtuous man called Mahu, in a bowl of washing water. As Mahu plunged in his hands, the fish cried out, 'Save me and I shall save you!' He warned Mahu of the coming flood, and in return Mahu gently placed the fish in a pot of water.

"It grew. He moved it to a larger pot, then to a trough. It grew and grew. Mahu moved it to a lake, then to the sea itself.

"The fish continued to grow as Mahu watched it swim away. Then he turned his energies to building an ark … Yes, yes, just like Noah's.

"When the ark was built, the flood set it afloat. It spun helplessly on the choppy water until up swam that same little fish – grown to gigantic size now, with a horn like a swordfish. 'Throw a rope round my horn,' said the fish, and it towed Mahu, over sunken mountains and drowned hills, to a place where life could begin again.

"The floodwaters receded. Mahu looked out over the sodden world emptied of people and felt his loneliness like a pain. So Vishnu gave him a wife, and from that marriage the present population of the world is descended.

"More than lives were lost during that flood. The gods' supply of nectar was washed away. Since the nectar's magic made them immortal the loss was a terrible one. For once, gods and demons formed an alliance and worked together to make more. They took the snake Ananta and, using him like a rope, lashed him round holy Mount Mandara. Then they pulled on head and tail, head and tail, until the mountain twirled like a gigantic paddle and churned the sea into a maelstrom. Vishnu changed into a tortoise and lifted the mountain on his back, so that it could spin on his bony

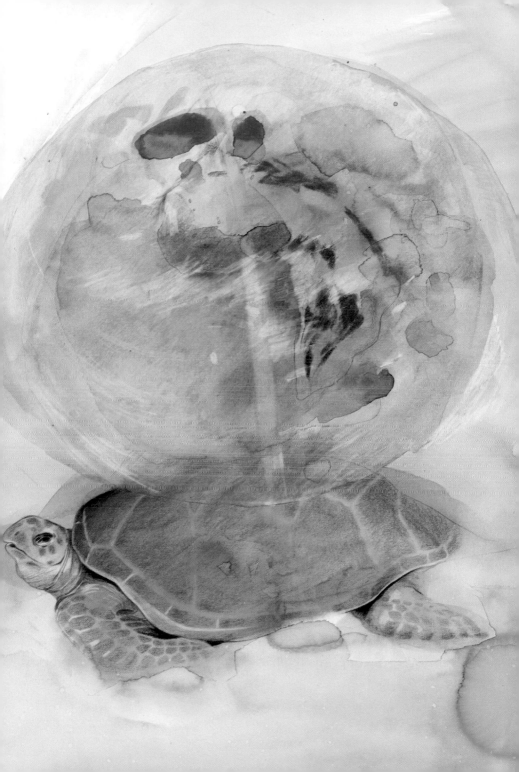

shell. Drops of magical nectar sprayed off every wave peak of the churning sea. Otherwise the gods would have died out long ago.

"There was a demon, Yaksha, who at the time of his making said to the Great Creator, 'Please, Brahma, don't send me out into the world defenceless. I'm so afraid of all the beasts and monsters you've made. I won't get five paces before I'm eaten by a lion … '

"'No lion shall kill you,' Brahma promised.

"' … or a tiger.'

"'No tiger shall kill you.'

"' … or a snake or a man.'

"'No snake or man shall kill you.'

"' … or a monster.'

"'No monster shall kill you.'

"Yaksha went on listing dangerous animals all day and half the night. Then, when he was satisfied that the world was a safe place for him, he went away, sniggering behind his paw. 'You forgot the boar!' Brahma called after him, but he did not hear. He was too busy plotting how to take over the world, terrorise the people and destroy the work of Creation. What could stop him? He began to shovel the land back into the water, and the world got smaller and smaller, the sufferings of men and women greater than ever before. They cried out, 'Help us! Save us, O Vishnu Great Preserver!'

"So Vishnu descended to Earth once more … this time in the shape of a boar. 'Stop, Yaksha! I have come to put an end to your cruelties!'

"'Oh yes? How? I'm indestructible! No living thing can kill me!'

"'Except a boar, which you forgot', said the boar. With one bristling, snorting, tusky charge, Vishnu ended Yaksha's reign of terror.

"So the *next* demon to ask a favour of Brahma made more sure of his wording. 'Grant, O Lord Creator, that no one shall kill me by night or day, either indoors or out.'

"Armed with this infallible protection, away went Yakasipu and persecuted devout Hindus most cruelly – even his own son. The son called out to Heaven. 'Help us! Save us, O Vishnu, Great Preserver!'

"So Vishnu descended to the Earth again ... this time as a lion. He killed Yakasipu on the threshold of his palace – neither indoors nor out – at dusk when it was neither day nor night.

"The war between demons and gods rumbled on over the centuries. Only once did the demons gain such an upper hand as to capture the Holy Mountain of Meru. Led by King Bali, they drove all the gods and goddesses off its sacred terraces. The homeless gods cried out to Vishnu: 'Help us! Save us, O Vishnu, Great Preserver!'

"So Vishnu once more came down from Heaven, disguised as a little holy man and calling himself Vamana.

"Now not even Bali was so depraved as to refuse charity to a holy man, especially when Vamana asked for so little: just a patch of ground to call his own – 'as much as I can cover in three strides.'

"As virtual owner of the whole world, Bali felt he could afford to be generous with a patch of dirt. So he granted Vamana his request.

"In the same instant, Vamana expanded, like an exploding star, into a giant of such size that the shadow of one finger cast darkness over King Bali. In one stride, he stood on the peak of Mount Meru. In the second stride, he left it far behind. In the third stride, having crossed over every grain of soil held by demon troops, he trod on Bali's head until the demon king surrendered.

"So the *next* demon to ask a favour of the gods took more care his trick should succeed. 'Grant, O Lord, that I shall never die at the hands of either god or demon.' Armed with this impregnable magic, Ravana the Ten-Headed-One waged war on gods, holy men and the people without pity. The people cried out aloud, 'Help us! Save us, O Vishnu, Great Preserver!'

"So Vishnu descended to Earth once again. This time he did not take on the power of an animal or even of a holy man. He became a common man – simply flesh and blood.

"'Stop, Ravana! I have come to put an end to your wickedness!'

"'Oh yes! And how will you do that? I'm beyond reach of god and demon – so how do you think *you*, a sorry little man, are going to stand in my way?'

"'Your pride will be your downfall, Ravana,' Vishnu said. 'For in your arrogance you thought Man too insignificant to worry about. You asked no protection from *him*. So it is Man who will kill you.' So saying, he cut off each of Ravana's ten heads and left them on the ground like stony ruins to be overgrown with weeds.

"You see? We humans have good cause to thank Vishnu. And yet it is not the boar nor the fish we Hindus chiefly love: not the little holy man nor the lion. We love Vishnu for two later visits he made to Earth.

"He came in the persons of Krishna and Buddha, whose lives were perfect in every way. While he was here, Krishna set us the perfect pattern for life. He wrote our holy literature and taught us how to worship the gods faultlessly. Then Buddha came and rescued those whose lives had gone wrong, teaching them how to put them right.

"At present Vishnu sleeps on the coils of the Great Snake Anantu whose thousand-hooded heads canopy his dreams. But he will come again, of course, when the world is in need of him. Next time he will wear the name 'Kalki'. It will be soon. Already we are passing through the last of the Four Ages – the darkest one, when humankind forget the gods and think so much about *owning* things that they never give a thought to their souls.

"There will be no demons to rescue us from this time. In fact there will be no saving of people, for they will refuse to be saved. The only solution will be to destroy everything, everyone, and begin again. Vishnu is also Shiva the Destroyer.

"After the destruction, when the whole of matter has dissolved back into the primeval ocean, a lotus flower with a thousand petals of pure gold will float to the surface once again. Its leaves will unfold to reveal Brahma the Creator. The circle is without end, you see. Creation-Preservation-Destruction-Renewal.

"Perhaps the destruction has already begun, and that's why we are here," mused the Hindu peaceably.

CHAPTER 12
Climbing up

The Navaho Indian squaw took off the blanket from round her shoulders and laid it out for them to see the pattern. Arcs and chords of black, white, red and turquoise joined the centre to the edges. A parade of insects, animals and human figures tropped round the border carrying baskets and reeds, pots and bundles as if on some everlasting journey.

"Deep down in the dark, at the beginning of time, nine creatures crept about an empty, bare, small cavern, without light or food. There were three kinds of beetles and six kinds of ant. One day they decided to look for something, somewhere better.

"So, in the centre of their dingy world, they built a hogan – a beehive-shaped hut four storeys high – and went indoors. Now the hogan was magic, for though they had built the outside, the inside was a new place where they had never been. Climbing up to the second floor, they blundered about in the darkness, feeling their way round the walls. It was bigger than the room below but seemed no better a place to live.

"'I've forgotten my pots!' exclaimed Pot-Carrying Beetle and hurriedly went back down to fetch them.

"Suddenly one of the beetles collided with a muddle of spiny legs and large, crackling wings. Two Locust People were already living in the chamber. 'Let's get out of here,' said everyone, and the ants, beetles and locusts all climbed up to the third floor.

"Nothing. But as they stumbled about in the dark, they heard footsteps on the ceiling. So they all agreed to climb to the topmost room of the hogan. There they found wonders which made all their building and climbing worthwhile. By the dull gleam of precious stones heaped in baskets they could dimly make out three men, three women, a boy and a girl. There was a yellowish dog, too, muttering and mumbling and chasing its tail.

"'What are you doing here?' asked First Man as their heads emerged through his floor.

"'Climbing up,' said the insects.

"'I've forgotten my pots!' cried Pot-Carrying Beetle and hurriedly went back for them.

"'You'd better join us then. We had just decided to do the same,' said First Woman.

"'But this is the topmost floor! We know. We built this hogan. We're already at the very top of the world,' said the beetles.

"'Then let's find another!'

"First Man went and breathed hard – *haaah* – on his heaps of magic treasure. From all the baskets bubbled columns of cloud, arching overhead. From the centre basket, a pillar of cloud funnelled up into the blackness overhead.

"'Grab hold!' barked the yellow, dog-like animal and sank his teeth into the pillar. All the rest – hanging on by crooked leg, sticky tongue, hand or tail – clung to the central pillar and rose through the roof of the hogan and out into a new world.

"It was as if fires were burning all around, for the new world flickered red. In it lived Sphinx Moth Man and Sphinx Moth Woman, beautiful in the veiny splendour of their wings.

"'I've forgotten my pots!' cried Pot-Carrying Beetle and hurriedly went back for them.

"'What are you all doing here?' asked Sphinx Moth Man as their heads emerged through his floor.

"'Climbing up,' said the ants. 'What must we do to get higher?'"

"'I am big in body but my wisdom is small. I don't know about these things,' said Sphinx Moth Man.

"Again they asked him. 'What must we do to get higher?'

"'I am big in body but my wisdom is small. I don't know about these things.'

"'You live here, don't you? You must know.'

"'I am big in body but my wisdom is small. I don't know … '

"'Offer him a present,' whispered the yellow dog. So First Man offered the Sphinx Moth Man a basket of smoke which the creature crammed into his mouth like spun sugar, pouching it in his cheeks. Then he blew a little over each traveller in turn and – lo and behold! – they rose up off the floor. Up and up and up they rose into a second chamber of the Red World.

"It was a frightening, dangerous place. The ground quaked and the walls shook. So the travellers quickly crowded aboard a flat red-and-white stone and soared upwards still further.

"Now the second Red World had three storeys in all. In the topmost room lived the Cat People. The visitors arrived in the very middle of a war and, as they poked up their heads, felt arrows whistle by and heard the eerie yowling and screeching of cats.

"'I've forgotten my pots!' exclaimed Pot-Carrying Beetle and hurriedly went back for them.

"'Kill! Kill! Kill!' chanted the Cats. They turned their bows on First Man. He only laughed and stood up fearlessly amid the swarm of arrows. He was dressed in armour – hide tunic and breeches so stiff with magic that the arrows simply bounced off him and fell to the floor. He waded in among the army of Cat People and swung them about by their tails, before piling them in a lifeless heap.

"The arrows stopped like an April shower, gone in an instant. There was a terrible silence except for some quiet, pitiful mewing. 'Give me a sacred song and I might undo what's done,' demanded First Man ferociously.

"Querulous voices broke into song. Not just the cats sang but the insects too, making a present of their magic songs to First Man. They had never seen him look so fierce before.

"After a time, a change came over him and he leaned across each dead cat and kitten, breathing on them until a tail stirred, an ear flickered, and each one rolled back on to its paws. Soon the Cat People were crowding round First Man as friendly as can be.

"But the yellowish dog had been looking round. 'This place is no good,' he reported back. 'Suffering and misery everywhere: famine, violence, earthquakes.'

"'I don't want my pots broken!' exclaimed Pot-Carrying Beetle anxiously. 'Let's get out of here!'

"'But we're at the top of the world, aren't we?' said the ants.

"'Then let's find another!'

"So First Man took some lightning, a rainbow and a ray of sunshine and made the rafters of a ceiling. Then he took out a magic wand which he planted in the centre of the chamber, stamping the soil firm around its base. Where he left his footprints, the travellers went and stood holding on to the wand as best they could. They burst upwards out of the fiery Red World and into another above it.

"Pillars of light to East, West, North and South showed them the new place. It was as if this world were built on sand, for the light was yellow and the ground crunched under their feet. But the sand proved to be salt. The only people living there were Old Salt Man, Old Salt Woman and Fire God. Wriggling through the drifts of salt were snakes of every colour and pattern.

"'I've left my pots behind!' exclaimed Pot-Carrying Beetle and hurriedly went back for them.

"Off went the yellow dog, sniffing here, sniffing there, poking his nose into every corner of the Yellow World. 'Hmm. Just as I thought. This place is evil,' he reported back. 'No place for us. Best keep going.'

"'Who does he think he is?' hissed the snakes. 'Does he have no respect for anyone, your yellow doggy friend?'

"First Man set about building a new hogan – a beautiful white house supported by five poles. Everybody crowded inside – Salt Man and Salt Woman and most of the Snake People too. They waited, but nothing happened. They sang all the songs they knew, but still they stayed where they were.

"'Have we reached the top then?' asked the people. 'Is there nowhere else to go?'

"'Where's that nosy dog of yours?' asked one of the snakes.

"From outside the hogan came an angry snarl. 'That's right! Call me names! Insult me! But you can sing all the songs in the Red and Yellow World: you won't get any higher without my help.' You see, the animal was really a great deal more magic than anyone supposed. Besides, he had tied great knots in the rising columns of light to North, South, East and West; not even a bird could have flown upwards just then.

"They offered him presents, but he simply sat with his nose on his tail. 'What our friend needs is a name,' said First Man loudly, 'so that people can treat him with the respect he deserves.' The dog's ears pricked up. 'I shall call him "He-who-causes-the-light-to-rise," and then perhaps he will help us.'

"Off went the yellow dog in a cloud of flying salt and untied the knots in the columns of light. Up went the ants and beetles; up went First Man and First Woman, children and dog. Up went the Cat People and snakes, Old Salt Man and Old Salt Woman and Fire God. 'Where are we going now?' they all asked.

"'Somewhere better!' they all said by way of reply.

"The next world was blue, with mountains to North, South, East and West. The ground was not dull and flat, but rolled and dipped in gentle hills. There were four great rivers full of fish, and blue-needled forests teeming with animals.

"Two wolves and two mountain lions greeted the travellers as they emerged out of the ground at a spot called White Speck of Earth. They were the Chiefs of the Blue World. 'What are you doing here?'

"'Climbing up,' replied the travellers, but it seemed as if they had reached at last somewhere they could stay and be happy. 'I even remembered my pots,' said Pot-Carrying Beetle.

"For seven years they camped on this piece of land. They played games and talked. They got to know each other – some so well that they married. And He-who-causes-the-light-to-rise taught them how to have babies. (He knew some very useful things, that yellow dog.)

"Over the years, everyone got used to the sight of yellow dog running about, making mischief, getting under their feet. It did not occur to them that he had no mate or children and must be lonely. One day, he found a baby at the place called Floating-Water. Wrapping it in a ray of sunlight, he sneaked it away: a child of his very own! He hid it near his heart, and swallowed its voice, so that no one would hear it crying.

"But the baby really belonged to the river, and the river ran wild with grief. It rose up and shed tears, breaking its banks and spilling into fields and homes. Hogans were washed away, tools and pots were swept downriver, and the rising floods chased the people to high ground. 'We'll all be drowned!' they wailed. Only by squeezing into two tall hollow reeds and climbing upwards did they escape the rising water.

"'It's all the fault of that yellow mutt!' cried Locust Man. 'I heard the river saying its child had been stolen by a yellow dog.'

"Everyone looked at the thief. His ears drooped, his tail curled between his legs and he let loose the baby's cry. The child fell from near his heart. First Man caught it and laid it on the silver, sobbing river, along with a peace-offering of jewels. 'We have climbed up this far: let's keep on until we reach somewhere higher, somewhere better,' he said.

"'But we are at the top of the Blue World now!'

"'Then let's go on to another!'

"Getting into the next world did not prove easy. 'We can't get out!' cried the first to reach the world's roof.

"'Smash your way through!' called those below. So they lammed out with fists and sticks, beaks and feet until they made a hole.

"Water cascaded down on to their heads – cold water – and over the rim of the hole gawped the hideous faces of sea monsters.

"'I've definitely forgotten my pots!' exclaimed Pot-Carrying Beetle and slid back down the reed.

"Quickly, Spider Ant wove a brightly coloured web over the yawning hole. The leak was stemmed, the monsters could only chew on the strands and growl down at the travellers. First Man summoned four winds.

"After four days of blowing, these dried up the water overhead and drove the monsters away. Nervously, the travellers crept into the next world and looked around.

"That is how the people emerged into this world of ours. Pot-Carrying Beetle, in going back for his pots, decided to stay on in the lower world, manufacturing dreams and getting ready a resting place for the dead.

"'Here we are and here we want to stay,' said the people. So First Man built one last Creation Hogan, and in it made Sun and Moon and Seasons. When he had finished, the Sun stood still in the sky, and the seasons would not change. Like a wheel stuck in the mud, the years refused to turn. Everyone looked at the yellow dog. 'He-who-causes-the-light-to-rise … ' they began.

"'That's not my name.'

"'What is it then? Rover? Roamer-about?'

"'No. That's not my name either.'

"'You tell us off a lot. We'll call you Scolder,' they suggested.

"'But that's not my name.'

"'You shall be "White-Coyote-Howling-in-the-Dawn,"' said First Man.

"Coyote wagged his tail; he liked that name. So he sat back and gave a great bark. The Sun and Moon moved at last. The wavering sky set, like milk curding into cheese. 'Now go and live your lives,' said First Man. 'Our journey is done.' The people picked up their tools and bags of seed. The ants and beetles crawled away. The birds took to the trees, the snakes to the rocky places, the moths to the moonlight.

"But that night, no one could sleep for the distant crying of a child. No one knew whose the child was, or how to find it. After the earlier flood, they were frightened by the sound. So First Man and First Woman went out searching, and did not stop searching until they found a baby girl cradled on a rainbow. The cords of her hammock were sky-blue, dawn-bright, twilight and turquoise.

She was the daughter of Mother Darkness and Father Dawn. When First Man took her gently in his arms, he found a small white wind in her right ear and small dark wind in her left.

"Her name was Changing Woman. They fed her on pollen until, in just eighteen days, she grew to adulthood. It is she, and not First Man, who brings anything new into being nowadays. She is more powerful, her magic even more wonderful than he who led us from the deep-down dark out into the shining world."

"I wove it myself," said the Navaho Indian woman, folding up her blanket once more. "My spirit was in it while I worked. Look here is the line I wove from the centre to the edge, to let my spirit escape when it was done. Otherwise my wits would be trapped inside the blanket, and I would be a crazy woman now."

"If you think that's how the world began," said the Egyptian, "then I'd say you already were."

CHAPTER 13
Ship of a million years

"Before the time of the gods, the universe was filled with water: a great stagnant wealth of water without shore, without bed, without a surface. The ocean was called Nun," said the Egyptian. "Though there was no life, the will to live existed – a wish so strong that it stirred up the waters. A flower appeared in the water. A white lotus floated upwards, its flower tight shut in a ball, cushioned on a wreath of leaves. When the flower opened, there, crouched at its heart was a small boy. He was curled up, his legs and arms drawn in, head tucked against his chest. This was Amun.

"He had only one eye – but what an eye! For he could send it here and there to do his bidding. When the Eye was open, daylight glimmered dimly around it; when it was shut, there was night once more, as black as ever. Finding nowhere solid to stand, Amun created a hill to stand on.

"Being first in the world, Amun had no wife, of course, and no one to marry. Besides, who would have been worthy of such a husband? So Amun married his own magnificent shadow. And gathering the saliva in his mouth, he spat it out – *Ptha! Ptha!* – to make children: a son, Shu and a daughter, Tefnut. In the chaos and darkness, they slipped down – *splash!* – and were swept away into the dark, swirling seascape. Amun went after them a step or two, but then lost sight of them among the pitching waves. 'Oh my children! Eye! Find my children, Eye! Search every fathom. Find them!' Amun took his one eye from its socket and set it on the sea.

"Small and shining, it floated over the tossing waters, searching the furrows between each wave and the deeps below. Finally, it found Shu and Tefnut, clinging to one another, floundering and barely alive. They grasped hold of its long, dark lashes and it drew them home to the island hill.

"As they approached, they saw the island lit by a strange glow. The Eye began to feel uneasy. Its worst fears were confirmed when it saw Amun. For in its absence he had created himself a new eye, brighter and more shining than the first. At least it meant Amun was able to see his children climbing up the hill towards him. At the sight of them he wept great tears of gratitude. As each tear touched the hill, a person sprang up; a man or woman or child: the whole human race, in fact.

"'Is that all the thanks I get?' said the roving Eye, filling with tears of its own – tears of grief. 'To be supplanted by another?'

"'No, no!' exclaimed Amun. 'For you were with me from the first, and you have saved my beloved son and daughter. In future I shall wear you in my forehead, above the other, and you shall rule this new world of men and be called Ra, the Sun God. But hurry now for we have made people, but no world for them to live in!' Turning to Shu and Tefnut, he said, 'Today, children, you shall marry. Though you are brother and sister, you shall be man and wife, and your children shall be the makers and shapers of the Earth.'

"After the marriage, Tefnut gave birth to a son, Geb the Ground, and a daughter, Nut the Sky. Just as any father lifts his daughter up to ride on his shoulders, Shu raised his daughter to ride in splendour above all Creation. She lay stretched from one horizon to the other, in robes of cornflower blue trimmed with fleecy cloud. Geb spent his time floating on his face in a circular sea below her. Regions of his back were red – hot, desert dunes peopled by fierce nomads. Down the centre, in the hollow of his spine, the land was black and muddy, soft and fertile. There the people of Egypt lived, grew crops and worshipped the gods who shared their world with them.

"For a time, you see, the gods lived on the earth. They ruled with perfect wisdom and there were no disputes, no wars, no injustice. But after a time they left, having set men and women an example to live by, to ride out eternity in the Ship-of-a-Million-Years.

"The ship belongs to Ra, the Sun God. In it, he and the other gods sail the sky. The stars bring him breakfast each morning, and wash his face. Then he sets sail from the eastern horizon towards the West. After dark, the ship sails on down into the Underworld, and travels the darklands as it has just travelled the sky, visiting the Kingdom of the Dead.

"One day the waters of Nun may rise up again and swallow the world, just as the Nile rises each year, flooding its banks. In the meantime, the eye of Amun watches over us as tenderly as it watched over the children of the Creator before the world was even made."

CHAPTER 14

Tethering post of the stars

At night, the Maori and the Fon of Abomey, the Egyptian and the Siberian would lie awake trying to make sense of the stars; people as well acquainted with the night sky as the creases of their own palms. But either low cloud blotted out the constellations, or else the sparkling lights appeared juggled and jumbled.

It upset the scientist, too, though he showed his unease in little bursts of nasty spleen. "Call yourselves navigators? You couldn't find a ship in a bottle!" They looked at him with uncomprehending grief and asked him, if he knew any better, to advise them.

The Siberian Yakut, however, with his hatchet-shaped face, spoke with reassuring certainty when he said, "It's just that the cords have snapped that used to tether the stars to the Great Tree."

"At the start – only sea. And the Milk-White Lord of Creation moving over the face of the water. Though the universe existed already, nothing was to be seen. Only the Milk-White Lord of Creation and one demon. The Demon was floating in a pod over the sea's surface, thinking how he might rule over the Universe – like us on our raft.

"When the Milk-White Lord saw the shrivelled little pod, he called out to the Demon: 'Where have you come from? Nowhere that will be, is.'

"'That's all you know,' jeered the Demon. 'I come from the ground hidden under the water.'

"'What land? There isn't any land! What a liar! What a fibber!' The Milk-White Lord roared with laughter. 'No such place!'

"The Demon grew agitated. His pod-boat rocked violently. 'Oh yes there is! There's ground enough down there to stand a throne on – *my* throne!'

"'Prove it! Don't believe there's enough for a fish to perch on!'

"With a curse and a splash, the demon stepped over the edge of his boat and dived down. Within an hour he had returned with a sackful of earth, which he proceeded to open and throw at the Milk-White Lord in muddy fistfuls.

"The Lord caught each handful and floated it on the sea, until an island began to form, and then he seated himself on it … just like us on our raft.

"The angry Demon swam to the edge of the mud-heap to snatch hold of the Creator's robe and drag him into the sea. When his talons could not reach, he thought instead to claw the earth from under him. 'Give that back. It's *my* mud. You can't have it.' But instead of pulling the island to pieces, he only succeeded in stretching the shoreline, stretching its clay into a greater and greater island. The more the demon worried at it with teeth and claws and hooked feet, the more the island-world grew until it was the size of a continent.

"In the very centre, the Milk-White Lord stood on a high hill, his hands on his hips, watching with pleasure. Then he stirred himself to the task of Creation.

"At the foot of the hill he filled a lake with white magic milk. At the peak of the hill he planted a tree which grew and grew to a size beyond human imagination. In time, the tree spread out its

branches at seven different heights, so that its boughs formed the eaves and joists of the seven-tiered Heaven. The tree plunged its roots down into the realms of demons, extending the kingdom of the Milk-White Lord deep into the ocean of darkness and evil.

"Good spirits made their houses there, using the tree's roots as pillars and roof-beams. Soon the Universe below the earth and the Universe above the Earth were all built to the design of the Milk-White Lord, and peopled by spirits, according to his plans.

"While the spirits inhabit each thing, it has the power to live. When they choose to move out, that tree or river or ox or woman dies. But there have, in the history of the world, been men who drank from the magic milk-lake. Their strength was past even that of the spirits and their bravery was a hundred times greater than ordinary men.

"After riding about the completed world, the Milk-White Lord tethered his horse to the Great Tree and climbed up it to perform one last task. He used the outermost twigs of the outermost branches to tether the newly made stars in place. And that is why they have held to their constellations from that day to … well, until this."

"Where did the demon go?" asked someone.

The Yakut was slow to answer. They heard him swallow hard before speaking. "All the evil spirits were forced to retreat as far as the Gulfs of Ice. And there they wait, ravening with hunger, for the great waters of the world to spill over into their mouths and bring them their meat."

"What meat?"

The Yakut swallowed hard again. "Any unfortunate fools who venture too far out from dry land – and drown … Like us on this raft."

CHAPTER 15
The smallness of mankind

"While I listen," said a sage old Chinaman, "I am like a man looking into a windblown pond. I recognise certain pieces – this is my eye, this is my ear – though the whole is unfamiliar.

"I recognise, for instance, the egg of which the Japanese lady spoke, and I recognise the giant of which the Viking told us. It is to be expected, I suppose. The Chinese themselves tell a thousand different versions of any story: we are so many and our views of the world are so varied."

"We, too, believe that before the world existed, there was an egg. The egg hatched, and its two halves separated because they were of different substances. All that was light and airy rose up. All that was heavy and dense sank down. The Earth that was formed was square, the sky above it round. For all matter is either of the family 'ying' or the family 'yang'. *Yang* and *ying* are opposites in every way. But like the two halves of a broken plate, one is useless without the other.

"Out of the egg hatched Pangku, a barbarous dwarf dressed in leaves, to crouch between the ground and the low ceiling of the world. Every day he grew three metres taller, but the world grew too – thicker the crust, higher the sky – so that Pangku never banged his head. For seven million days he grew and the world grew to accommodate him. He even fashioned it, after a fashion.

"But it was a bare, grim place. When Pangku was sullen, the weather was bitter and wild. Only when Pangku was happy was the weather tinged with summer.

"One morning, the weather knew to be neither one thing nor another – for Pangku lay dead along the ground. His last breath was the first wind, travelling the square Earth in an endless ellipse. His last word became the thunder.

"As for his body, it broke down into a thousand new things. His left eye became the sun, his right the moon. His blood became the rivers, lakes and seas, his veins and nerves the strata in the rocks. His flesh decayed into the rich soil of pasture and plain, and his hair into plants and trees. Every precious jewel or worthless rock derives from his teeth and bones, and his sweat turned to rain.

"As for humankind, well, our ancestors were once the fleas and lice which made Pangku itch.

"The world was not allowed to keep all the gifts of Pangku. Soon a gigantic monster, Gong-gong, appeared on the Earth. It rampaged about, but failing to conquer the Earth took out its anger on Bu Zhou, holy mountain of the North-West. It's gnarled horns shattered the mountain to rubble. The sharp peak, as it fell, tore a gaping gash in the sky and down poured all the waters above, sluicing away the tiny people living below. Every last one was drowned.

"Yes, we too saw a flood, you see – an End of the World. Only after the flood did the goddess Nugua appear on Earth to put right the damage done by Gong-gong.

"The sun could not shine in the north-west region of the sky, for there was no sky to shine in. A new source of light had to be found. One day a blazing dragon, red as heat, sprang up out of the rubble of Mount Bu Zhou and spread its scarlet wings across the holed sky. When it breathed out there was icy cold; its breathing in was summer.

"With the dragon installed in the north-western sky, Nugua set about recreating the human race. She sat down amid wet yellow clay and began to mould perfect, little dolls. It was enthralling work at first – a challenge to see what variety of pretty faces and elaborate clothes she could sculpt. But after a time, the work grew tedious and Nugua grew bored. Row upon row of little dolls lay on the ground, and still there were hardly enough to people a village , let alone the whole world.

"So Nugua stood up, took the cord from round her robe and trailed it through the wet mud. Now and then she paused to let the slurry drip off the belt in little whorls and pats.

"When she added the vital ingredient of *ying* and *yang,* her first, beautiful clay models rose up and swaggered about, resplendent in rich robes and lovely to look at. 'You are nobility, princesses and philosophers,' said Nugua 'The best.'

"She gave life, too, to the whorls and pats of mud, but did not deign to speak to them. She did not tell them that they were to be the peasants and workers, the beggars, the cripples, the nobodies. They found that out for themselves soon enough.

"Other steps were taken to mend the damage done by Gong-gong the monster. There is a story told of a star maiden, Zhi nu, who wove the cloth of Heaven day by day. She must have been working to patch the tear.

"Her loom stood on the banks of the River of Heaven – the Milky Way – and on the far bank a star youth, Quian niu, tended his oxen in lonely fields of dark. The two would often cast longing looks across the glistening river until, at last, their love would not be denied another day. Zhi nu crossed over and married Quian niu.

"Married life brought such bliss to the two lovers that they

burned all the brighter in the sky: as bright as comets. But they had time only for each other, none for their work. The oxen strayed unattended. They fell into ditches of dark. The loom that had once woven the blue of the sky stood idle.

"Heaven grew irritable, then angry. 'Return to your loom at once, Zhi nu! Once a year you may visit Quian niu. Once a year and no more!'

"That is why, on the seventh night of the seventh month, all the birds of the world fly high into the sky and make of their outstretched wings a bridge across the milk River of Heaven. The bride runs softly across it and into the arms of her husband."

"Cows! snakes! beetles! Now it's lice and fleas! And pats of mud!" raged the scientist, unable to keep silent another moment. "What is it with you people? We can put astronauts on the Moon, build computers and satellites, cure diseases, destroy the planet at the touch of a button – and all you do is harp back to some mythical beginning that never happened, when we were all lice or spiders or half-wits! Haven't any of you heard of Evolution? Don't any of you have a rational mind? Are you all superstitious idiots?"

The Chinaman listened with patience, then looked around him at four horizons unbroken by land, cloud or ship. "Each time I am tempted to think that my life is something weighty in the scales of history, I remind myself of the size of mountains, the spread of seas, the length of time and the beauty of nature. I can hardly help but see the truth. In the cosmos, I am smaller than a lash in the lid of Pangku, and my life is over in a blinking. Is it not useful, now and then, to remember the scale of things? The vastness and volume and depth of the oceans, the height of the planets, the endless corridors of time? The smallness of 'man'?"

The scientist seemed unwilling to answer. "Very well, sir," said the Hindu. "Tell us how it really happened. In the eyes of Science. Tell us how the world began."

CHAPTER 16
Out of time

"Well, I mean what are we talking about here? The beginning of the Universe? Formation of the Earth? It's just a planet, you know!" said the scientist. "One planet in one galaxy in a universe with millions of other galaxies. There was a gigantic explosion ten or twenty billion years ago. The pieces are still flying outwards from it. A piece of shrapnel from an exploding bomb – that's all the world is. Revolving around one middle-aged, average-size star. First the shrapnel was red-hot – molten. Then it cooled down – formed an atmosphere. Condensation. Huge areas of sea. And volcanoes still spewing up the molten magma. Hydrogen, methane, ammonia. That's all the ingredients you need for life, and there they were. Mix with water and – *hey presto!* – amino acids, the chief component of protein. And what's the chief component of life?"

"A soul," suggested the Hindu.

"Protein," snapped the scientist. "Add lightning or solar radiation, and the oceans turned into a fertile stew. That's how life came about. The simple cell, that's your First Man. Stromatolite, call him. Blue-green algae on a rock. Then there were fish.

"First the plants adapted to dry land. Then lifeforms in the ocean started pulling themselves ashore. And every time a catastrophe happened, some species would be wiped out but for a few of its freaks. That's how the species evolved: survival of the fittest combined with the accidental survival of freaks.

"Take the dinosaurs. Very successful until their environment changed. Two hundred million years, then one day – or one century, or one millennium – something put them out of business, and it was something else's turn. Currently it's ours. We're the latest superbeasts to inherit the Earth.

"We're so good at problem-solving, reasoning and tool-using, you see, that we've made ourselves masters of the planet. The day the world began there was no one there to see it. But scientists can look at the facts and say: that's how it was. No inventions. No fairy-tales. Just logic. That's how it was."

"But it doesn't say *why*," said the Hindu. "Your account tells us *how* the world began, but not *why*."

"There is no 'why'. I told you. It was an accident. No master plan. Just a series of accidents." The scientist was aggressive, as though the facts were his alone. "No cosmic *eggs!*" he said sneeringly.

"No? Even though you scientists describe the Earth to us as a thing with a yolk of fire and a broken shell of tectonic plates?"

"No primeval ocean then!" snapped the scientist.

"And yet you yourself said that all life came out of the sea!"

"No *monsters* roaming about, I mean."

"Unless, of course, you count two hundred million years of dinosaurs!"

"No holes torn in the sky by demons!"

"And yet what's this I hear about a hole in the ozone layer?"

"No Garden of Eden!"

"Not even your childhood, when everyday was sunny and you had done nothing so terrible that it could not be undone?"

"No order magically conjured out of chaos, I'm saying!"

"And yet you said yourself that the minds of humans have managed to analyse and make sense of everything around them: even the past and the future ... " said the Hindu. "The thing is, my dear logical friend, you listen to our stories with western ears. You take everything so literally. Your culture relies so much on facts and on words written down that you think words must always be taken literally. You listen to our stories as if they were newscasts. They are not newscasts, nor historical accounts. They are our myths. You see, myths can be a way of looking at things – full of symbols and signals and mind-pictures that generations of people have held in their imaginations."

"NO DIVINE PLAN!" yelled the scientist, pushing his face close up against the Hindu's. *"There's no God up there planning it!"*

The Hindu withdrew his face and wiped the scientist's spit off his cheek. "Ah then, there we do differ. And no amount of words will ever bridge the gulf between your accidental world and our created one."

The rest looked on with a kind of fascination, studying the scientist. How did he describe himself? A descendant of green algae? An assembly of amino acids? Perched on a piece of shrapnel hurtling outwards into infinite darkness, through infinite, silent time? And for no good purpose in the world? His face was ashen and his knuckles white where he clutched his knees to his chest – as if he were trying to carry himself to safety in his own arms, as if he was obliged to carry the weight of his own life. Which, of course, he was.

"What does it matter where we think we come from?" said the scientist eventually. "We're all headed the same way now. We're all going to die. And *that's* the end line to all your stories of gods and star-trees and climbing up and cows and coconut women."

"Oh, but that's the biggest difference of all," said the Chinese, "between you and us."

"I shall be a star in Heaven," said the Melanesian.

"I shall travel to the land of Osiris," said the Egyptian, "where the sun passes overhead at night."

"I shall eat from the ovens of Yomi, among my ancestors," said the Japanese girl.

"I shall herd fat cows in Heaven."

"I shall be with Jesus, my Saviour,"

"I shall await reincarnation – higher in the scale of living things, I hope – holier and wiser, too."

"My fate was written in the Golden Book of Heaven the day I was born," said the Yakut. "What comes has been coming all along."

"Perhaps my soul will find the Kingdom of Hua-hsu where there is no longing for life or fear of death … But for you, sir. For you the end is everlasting."

"At least I don't tell myself stupid fairy-tales then try to believe in them!" the scientist replied, tight-lipped.

"I shall hunt with my ancestors," said the Maori, "for surely the Dream Time has come back."

"The Dream Time, yes," said the Navaho woman, folding her blanket with the utmost care.

A keen wind caught the raft and spun it round. Somewhere a tide was turning. It whirled the world round and washed out of shape the Great Circles. The Present pasted itself, like a poster, to the sky. The wind swept together the leaves of the calendar

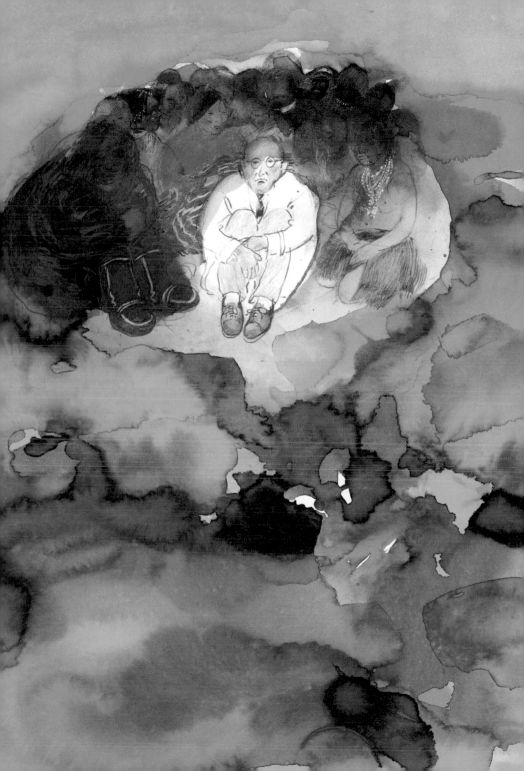

months and lightning burned them to ash. The ash fell like sleep on the eyelids of men and women everywhere, so that they dreamed they were floating, on icebergs, islands or rafts, across a bleak ocean – no land, no light, no life – on the day the world began.

And all their dreams were different. But most were a little the same.